STORY TRAIN

THE PROSE AND POETRY SERIES

MARJORIE PRATT
Director of Elementary Education, Spokane, Washington

MARY MEIGHEN
Seattle, Washington

Illustrated by
CAROL CRITCHFIELD
DON DENNIS, FRANK HULEFELD ASSOCIATES

Design by Stefan Salter

STORY
TRAIN

THE L. W. SINGER COMPANY

SYRACUSE   CHICAGO

Contents

STORIES AND POEMS

PLAYMAKING IS FUN

MORE STORIES AND POEMS

Timothy Turtle

Timothy Turtle lived in the woods
near a river.

He was a very big turtle.

All the animals that lived in the woods
knew him.

A frog that lived near the river
was Timothy's good friend.

"Timothy Turtle" adapted from *Timothy Turtle* by Alice Vaught Davis, copyright, 1940, by Harcourt, Brace and Company, Inc., and reprinted with their permission.

Sometimes Timothy would call,
"Little Frog, jump on my back.
I will give you a ride."
The little frog would jump
on Timothy's back and away they
would go.
There was a hill in the woods
near the river.
Timothy liked to climb up this hill
in the woods.
He liked to slide down the hill
into the river.

One morning Timothy wanted to see
his friend the frog.
Timothy started to slide
down the hill.

The hill was muddy.
Timothy went down the hill too fast.
Over he went on his back.
He could not turn over.
He tried and tried,
but he could not turn over.

Timothy Turtle was on his back
for a long time.
A squirrel who lived in a tree
by the river saw Timothy.
He saw Timothy trying to turn over.
He ran to Timothy and said,
"What happened?
Can I help you, Timothy?"

"Oh! Oh!" said Timothy Turtle.
"I went down the hill too fast.
I did not know that the hill
was muddy.
Over I went on my back.
Now I cannot turn over."

"I will help you," said the squirrel.
He tried and tried to turn Timothy over.
He could not do it.

"I will find someone to help me,"
said the squirrel.

Away he ran into the woods.

The squirrel met a rabbit in the woods.

"Good morning, little rabbit,"
he called.

"I want you to help me."

The rabbit stopped and said,
"What can I do for you?"

The squirrel said, "Timothy Turtle
went down a muddy hill.

He fell on his back.

Now he cannot turn over.

Come and help me turn him over."

The rabbit and the squirrel ran
to help Timothy.
They pulled and pulled.
They could not turn him over.
"I will find the woodchuck,"
said the squirrel.
"He is Timothy's friend.
I know he will help us
turn Timothy over."
Away went the squirrel to find
the woodchuck.

The squirrel saw the woodchuck
under a tree.

"Woodchuck!" called the squirrel.
"Come and help me.
Timothy Turtle went down a muddy hill.
He went too fast.
He fell on his back.
He cannot turn over.
The rabbit and I cannot turn him over.
Will you come and help us?"

"Yes, I will help you,"
said the woodchuck.

Off they ran to help Timothy Turtle.

The squirrel, the rabbit, and
the woodchuck pulled and pulled.
They could not turn Timothy over.

Timothy's friend, the frog, hopped
out of the water.
He saw the animals trying
to turn Timothy over.

The frog jumped up on a rock.
He called, "You cannot
turn Timothy over.
Take him by the tail.
Pull him down to the river.
He will turn over when he falls
into the water."

The squirrel pulled Timothy Turtle
by the tail.

The rabbit pulled the squirrel
by the tail.

The woodchuck pulled the rabbit
by the tail.

They all pulled and pulled.

At last they pulled Timothy
down to the river.

Into the water went Timothy Turtle.
Splash! Splash!
He turned over in the water.

He looked up at his friends and said,
"Thank all of you for helping me."

Who Am I?

1. I am Timothy's friend.
   I live near the river.
   Who am I?

2. I am Timothy's friend.
   I live in a tree.
   Who am I?

3. I helped pull Timothy to the river.
   I pulled the squirrel's tail.
   Who am I?

4. I helped pull Timothy to the river.
   I pulled the rabbit's tail.
   Who am I?

Chippy Chipmunk

Chippy Chipmunk lived
under a big rock in a field.

One day Chippy Chipmunk said,
"I have lived under this rock
for a long time.
I am going to move today."

"Chippy Chipmunk" adapted by permission from *Chipmunk Moves* by Margaret Friskey, copyright, 1946, by David McKay Company, Inc.

18

Chippy Chipmunk put three nuts
in his cheek.
He put some nuts in a bag.
He tied the bag to a stick.
Then he walked down the road.

"I want to live in an apple orchard,"
said Chippy to himself.
"I will find an apple orchard
and I will live there."

Chippy walked down the road.
He met Mr. Skunk.

"Hello, Chippy," said Mr. Skunk.
"Where are you going?"

Chippy took the three nuts
out of his cheek.
He put the stick and the bag
on the grass.
Then he said, "I am looking
for an apple orchard.
I want to live in an apple orchard."

Chippy put the three nuts back
in his cheek.
He picked up the stick and walked on.
Mr. Skunk went with him.

Soon Mr. Skunk and Chippy
met Gray Kitten.

"Where are you going?"
asked Gray Kitten.

"We are looking for an apple orchard,"
said Mr. Skunk.
"Chippy wants to move.
He wants to live in an apple orchard."

"Come and live with me, Chippy,"
said Gray Kitten.
"I live in that big house over there."

21

Chippy took the three nuts
out of his cheek.
He put the stick and the bag
down on the grass.

"No," he said, "I do not want
to live in a house.
I want to live in an apple orchard."

Chippy put the three nuts back
in his cheek again.
He picked up the stick with the bag
on it.
He went on down the road.

Gray Kitten went with Chippy
and Mr. Skunk.

Fuzzy Duck saw Chippy, Gray Kitten, and Mr. Skunk.

He called to them, "Where are you going?"

"We are looking for an apple orchard," said Mr. Skunk.

"Chippy wants to live in an apple orchard."

"Chippy may live in this big tree near the pond," called Fuzzy Duck.

Chippy took the three nuts
out of his cheek.
He put the stick and the bag
down on the grass.
Then he said, "I do not want to live
in a tree by the pond.
I want to live in an apple orchard."
Chippy put the three nuts back
in his cheek.
He picked up the stick and the bag.
He walked on down the road
with Gray Kitten and Mr. Skunk.
Fuzzy Duck came out of the pond.
He walked on with Chippy, Gray Kitten,
and Mr. Skunk.

At last Chippy saw an apple orchard.

"Here is an apple orchard," he said.

He took the nuts out of his cheek.

"This is where I will live," he said.

"A weasel lives near this orchard,"
said Mr. Skunk.

"You do not want to live here."

25

Chippy put the stick down.
He climbed up on the fence
that was around the apple orchard.

"This is where I will live," he said.
"I am not afraid of a weasel."

Chippy jumped down from the fence.
He began to dig in the orchard.
He worked all day to dig a hole
for his home.
He made a front door and a back door.
He put grass over each door.
He did not want the weasel to find
his home.

Then Chippy sat down under a tree
to look at his home.
He saw a big squirrel.

The squirrel walked over to Chippy.
He said, "You cannot live here.
Chipmunks cannot live in this orchard."

The weasel was outside the fence.
He heard what the squirrel said
to Chippy.
He said to himself, "I wish
I could get through this fence.
I want to get into the orchard."

The weasel looked around the fence.
At last he found a big hole
under the fence.
He ran into the apple orchard.

The weasel looked around the orchard.
He saw Chippy and the squirrel.

"What a fine dinner they will make
for me," he said.

Chippy looked up and saw the weasel.

"Run!" he called to the big squirrel.

"Here comes a weasel."

Chippy ran into his house as fast
as he could go.

The squirrel ran around a big tree.

The weasel ran after the big squirrel.

Around and around the tree they went.

Chippy looked out of his door.
He said to himself, "I am afraid
that weasel will catch the squirrel."
Chippy ran out of his house.
He called out, "Hi, Mr. Weasel!"
The weasel stopped.
He looked at Chippy.
Then he ran after Chippy.
Chippy ran this way and that way,
this way and that way.
Then he ran through a little hole
in the fence.

The weasel ran after Chippy.
He could not get through the little
hole in the fence.
Bump! Bump! he went into the fence.
"Oh, my head! My head!"
called the weasel.
"I will get out of this apple orchard.
I will go back to my home."

The next day Chippy went back
to his home in the apple orchard.
He saw the big squirrel under a tree.

"Chippy," the big squirrel said,
"you are a good friend.
I want you to live where I live."

32

Who Said?

1. Who said, "I am going to move today"?

2. Who said, "He wants to live in an apple orchard"?

3. Who said, "I live in that big house over there"?

4. Who said, "Chippy may live in this big tree near the pond"?

5. Who said, "Chipmunks cannot live in this orchard"?

6. Who said, "What a fine dinner they will make for me"?

7. Who said, "I will get out of this apple orchard"?

The Bunny

Once there was a bunny
And a green cabbage head.
   "I think I'll have some breakfast,"
This little bunny said.
So he nibbled and he nibbled,
Then cocked his ears to say,
   "I think that this is just the time
I should be hopping on my way."

Sleepyhead Bats

They hang by their toes
and they doze and doze,
drowsy old sleepyhead bats;
with the tops of their crowns
so upside down,
it's lucky they don't wear hats!

They fold up their wings,
the sleepy old things,
and dangle themselves about,
so it's lucky they go
without jackets, you know,
or their pockets would all spill out!

Aileen Fisher

"Sleepyhead Bats" reprinted by permission of the publishers, Abelard-Schuman, Ltd., from *Up the Windy Hill* by Aileen Fisher. Copyright, 1953, by Aileen Fisher.

The Run-Away Cows

Little Black Cow and Old White Cow
lived on a farm.

One day Old White Cow said, "I do not
like this farm. I have to eat grass
every day. I have to give milk
every day."

Little Black Cow said, "I do not want
to live here. I give milk every day.
I have nothing to eat but grass.
Let us run away from this farm."

"The Run-Away Cows" by James S. Tippett, from *Playing Together*, The Children's Bookshelf, edited by B. R. Buckingham, copyright, 1934, by Ginn and Company.

The two cows jumped over the fence.
They ran down the road. They did not
look back at the farm. They ran
down the road as fast as they could go.

They heard something say, "Look out!
Look out! I am an automobile.
This is my road. Get out of here or
I will run over you."

Old White Cow and Little Black Cow
were afraid. They jumped out
of the road. The automobile went by
very fast. Another automobile went by.
Then another automobile went by.

Old White Cow and Little Black Cow
had to walk on the side of the road.

"I do not like automobiles,"
said Little Black Cow.

"I do not like this road,"
said Old White Cow.

"I wish we could find something
to eat," said Little Black Cow.

"We cannot eat this grass by the side
of the road," said Old White Cow.
"It is too dry to eat."

The cows went on. They came
to a big green field. There was
a fence around the field.

"Look at the green grass
in that field," said Old White Cow.

"Let us eat some of it,"
said Little Black Cow.

The two cows jumped over the fence.
They began to eat the green grass
in the field.

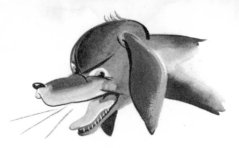

"Bow-wow! Bow-wow!" said a big dog.
"Get out of this field. This grass is
for the cows on this farm. Go back
to your home."

The two cows were afraid of the dog.
They jumped over the fence as fast as
they could go. They ran down the road.
On and on they ran.

At last Little Black Cow stopped.
She said, "I want to go home.
I want some green grass to eat.
I want some water to drink."

Old White Cow said, "I want
to go home, too. Where is our home?"

Little Black Cow and Old White Cow
went up one road and down another.
They did not know where to go.

"If I find my home I will never
run away again," said Old White Cow.

They heard a horse coming
down the road. A man was riding
on the horse. The man called,
"I have looked and looked for you
all day. Go home as fast as
you can go."

Away went Little Black Cow and
Old White Cow.

Away went the man on his horse.

41

The next day Old White Cow had green grass and water.

Little Black Cow had all the green grass she could eat.

They were very happy. They were at home.

"We will never run away again," they said.

Do You Know?

1. Little Black Cow and Old White Cow
wanted to run away from the farm.
   Why did they want to run away?

2. The cows ran down the road.
Something said, "Look out! Look out!"
   What was it?

3. The cows jumped over a fence
into a big green field. They began
to eat the green grass.
   Why did they run out of the field?

4. Little Black Cow and Old White Cow
ran and ran. They met a man riding
on a horse.
   What did the man say to the cows?

Words from the Story

automobile

dog

horse

field

The Fox and the Crab

One day a fox saw a little crab walking near a river. The fox stopped to look at the crab.

"Walk fast," said the fox. "You will never get very far walking the way you do."

"I can walk fast. I can run, too," said the crab.

"I would like to see you run," said the fox as he walked away.

"Come back!" called the crab.
"I want to run a race with you.
Then you will know that I can run."

"You cannot race with me," said
the fox. "You will soon find out
that all you can do is to walk."

The crab knew that the fox
could run fast. He said to himself,
"Look at the fox's long legs.
I cannot run a race with him.
Why did I tell him that I would run
a race with him?"

The crab looked at the fox's tail.
He said to himself, "I know what I
will do. I will play a trick
on this fox."

The crab walked over to the fox.
He said, "Some animals can run faster
when their tails are up. You have a
big tail. Will you keep your tail down
when we run the race?"

"I will keep my tail down," said
the fox. "Tie it down if you wish."

This was what the crab wanted
the fox to say.

"I will tie your tail down,"
said the crab. "I will tie a stick
to your tail."

The crab looked around for a stick.
He said, "Here is a stick, Mr. Fox.
I will tie it on your tail."

The fox said, "Tie the stick
on my tail."

The crab did not tie the stick
on the fox's tail. He caught the end
of the fox's tail with his claws.

The fox did not look around
to see what the crab was doing.
He was looking down the road
at a big tree.

"We will run to that big tree
down the road," said the fox.

"Run as fast as you can,"
said the crab. "I will be there
as soon as you will."

The fox put his head up and called,
"I will see you at the big tree."

Away he ran as fast as he could go
down the road.

Away went the crab on the end
of the fox's tail.

The fox ran so fast that the crab
could not see the road.

He could not see the grass.

He could not see the trees.

All that he could see was
the fox's tail.

Soon the fox was at the big tree.
The crab was there, too, but the fox
did not know it.

The crab let go of the fox's tail.
He went into the grass. He wanted
to see what the fox would do.

The fox looked down the road.
"Where is that crab?" he said.
"He will take all day to get here."

"Are you looking for me?"
said the crab as he walked out
of the grass. "I got here as soon as
you did."

The fox looked down at the little crab.
"How did you get here so soon?"
he said. "I never knew that a crab
could run so fast. The next time
that I run a race I will keep
my tail up."

Do You Know?

1. The fox looked at the crab and said, "You will never get very far walking the way you do."

Why did he think the crab could not get very far?

2. The crab said to the fox, "I want to run a race with you."

Why did the crab wish he had not said this?

3. The crab said to himself, "I will play a trick on this fox."

What did the crab do?

4. At the end of the race the fox was surprised to see the crab.

Why was the fox surprised?

Words from the Story

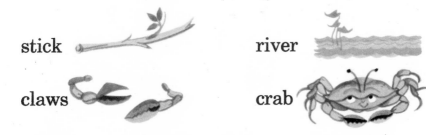

stick   river

claws   crab

The Sleepy Maple Trees

I think they must be sorry—
  The little maple trees—
That they go to bed too early to
  See holidays like these!

They never see Thanksgiving
  Nor Hallowe'en at all,
Because they all go fast asleep
  So early in the fall.

Poor little tired maples,
  Sleeping in the breeze,
They miss the greatest fun of all—
  They can't be Christmas trees!

Eleanor Hammond

Traveling

Mister Robin and his wife
   have started south once more,
They didn't shut a window,
   and they didn't lock a door!
They didn't take a traveling bag
   or lunch or anything!
Just took themselves! And said,
   "Cheer up! We'll be back next spring!"

Minnie Leona Upton

Hallowe'en

Hallowe'en's the time for nuts
And for apples, too,
And for funny faces that
Stare and glare at you.
Right behind them is a friend,
Jack or Bob or Bess,
Isn't it the greatest fun
When you try to guess?

Anna Medary

53

"Traveling" by Minnie Leona Upton, reprinted from *The Golden Flute* by Hubbard and Babbitt, published by The John Day Company.

"Hallowe'en" by Anna Medary from *Child Life Magazine*, copyright, 1926, by Rand McNally & Company.

Where Were the Rubbers?

One day Mrs. Goose could not find
her rubbers. She looked in the closet
where she always put her rubbers.
They were not there.

She looked all around the house.
She looked under all the chairs.
She could not find her rubbers.

Mrs. Goose said, "Where can my
rubbers be? I will go over
to Mrs. Pig's house. I will ask her
if she has seen my rubbers."

Mrs. Goose went to Mrs. Pig's house.
Mrs. Pig was coming out of her house.
She looked at Mrs. Goose.
"What can I do for you?" she said.

Mrs. Goose said, "I cannot find
my rubbers. I have looked and looked
for them. Have you seen my rubbers?"

"Your rubbers!" said Mrs. Pig.
"I have not seen your rubbers.
They would not be in my house.
Ask Mrs. Squirrel if she has seen
your rubbers."

Mrs. Goose said, "I will go
to Mrs. Squirrel's house. I will ask
her if she has seen my rubbers."

Mrs. Goose went to Mrs. Squirrel's
house.   She saw Mrs. Squirrel
under a tree.

"Oh! Mrs. Squirrel," called
Mrs. Goose, "I cannot find
my rubbers. I have looked all over
for them. Have you seen them?"

"No, I have not seen your rubbers,"
said Mrs. Squirrel. "Your rubbers
would not be in my house. Go home
and look in your house again.
I know that you will find
your rubbers there."

Mrs. Goose went back to her home.
She looked all around the house again.
She looked in her bed. She looked
under her pillow. She looked
in her closet again.

Then she went into her garden.
She looked all around the garden.
She began to dig in the garden.
She could not find her rubbers.

Mrs. Sheep came down the road.
She saw Mrs. Goose looking around
the garden. "What are you looking for?"
asked Mrs. Sheep.

"I am looking for my rubbers,"
said Mrs. Goose. "I have looked
all around my house. I have looked
all around my garden. I cannot find
my rubbers."

"Where do you keep your rubbers?"
asked Mrs. Sheep.

"I always put my rubbers in a bag
in my closet," said Mrs. Goose.
"My rubbers are not there now."

Mrs. Sheep looked at Mrs. Goose.
She said, "Why do you want
your rubbers now? It is not raining."

"It may be raining in the morning,"
said Mrs. Goose. "I want my rubbers
when it rains."

"Yes, it may rain," said Mrs. Sheep.
"I do not know where my rubbers are.
I will go home to look for them now."

Mrs. Goose went into her house again.
She looked and looked for her rubbers.
She looked in her big clock.
She looked behind all the doors.

At last Mrs. Goose said, "I will go
to bed. I may find my rubbers
in the morning."

The next morning Mrs. Goose heard
the rain coming down on the roof.

She looked out of a window.
There was water in the garden.
There was water in the road.
There was water everywhere.

Mrs. Goose said, "I have nothing
to eat in my house. I must go to town
today. I do not want to walk around
in the rain. I must find my rubbers.
Where did I put my rubbers?"

Mrs. Goose went to the closet.
She put on her coat. She put on
a little hat. She took her
big red umbrella out of the closet.

She walked out of the door
with the big red umbrella in her hand.

Mrs. Goose put up her big red umbrella.

Plop! Plop! Something fell
on the grass near Mrs. Goose.

She looked down.

There were her rubbers on the grass.

"Oh! Now I know what I did
with my rubbers," she said.

"I put them in my umbrella."

Do You Know?

1. Mrs. Goose looked and looked
for her rubbers.
Where did she look for them?

2. Mrs. Sheep said, "Why do you want
your rubbers now? It is not raining."
What did Mrs. Goose say?

3. The next morning Mrs. Goose heard
the rain coming down on the roof.
Why did she have to go out in the rain?

4. Mrs. Goose put on her coat and
her little hat. She put up her big red
umbrella. Then came a surprise.
What was the surprise?

Words from the Story

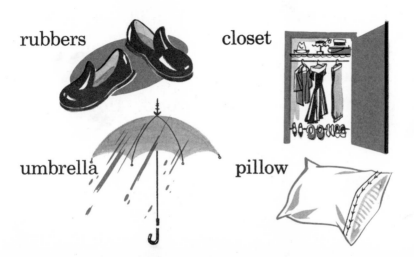

rubbers

closet

umbrella

pillow

65

Taper Tom

Long, long ago there was a princess
who was not happy. She never went out
of the castle. She sat by the window
all day. She never, never laughed.

The king did not know what to do.

"What shall I do?" he said. "How can
I make the princess happy? I want her
to laugh. I want her to know people.
I want her to see the world. How can
I make her happy?"

One day the king said to his soldiers,
"I want the princess to be happy.
I want her to laugh."

The king looked at his soldiers.
He said, "Find a man who can make
the princess laugh. He may have
the princess for his wife."

The soldiers went all over the world.
They looked and looked. They could not
find a man who could make
the princess laugh.

Taper Tom lived near the castle.
He heard about the princess.

"I will go to the castle,"
said Taper Tom. "I will see the king.
I will see the princess who will not
laugh. I will try to make her laugh.
I will take my pig with me."

Taper Tom went down the road. He met
a little old woman with a big goose.

"What a fine goose!" said Taper Tom.
"I wish I had that goose. I will
give you my pig for the goose."

"Give me your pig," said the old woman.
"You may have my goose."

The old woman gave Taper Tom the goose.
"It is a magic goose," said the woman.
"If anyone puts a hand on the goose,
you say, 'Come with me.' Then no one
can let go of the magic goose."

Taper Tom said, "What fun I will have
with this magic goose."

On went Taper Tom down the road.

Taper Tom looked at the magic goose.
He said, "I know what I will do.
I will give the magic goose
to the princess. Then the princess
will be happy, and the king will be
happy."

Taper Tom met a farmer. The farmer
looked at the goose.

"What a fine goose," said the farmer.
He put his hand on the goose.

"Come with me," said Taper Tom.

The farmer could not get away.
He tugged and tugged, but he could not
get away.

On went Taper Tom with the goose.
On went the farmer with Taper Tom.

A baker came down the road.
He looked at the farmer and
Taper Tom.

"Help! Help!" called the farmer.
"I cannot get away from this goose."
The baker ran to help the farmer.
He tugged and tugged at the farmer.

Taper Tom called, "Come with me."
The baker could not get away.

On went Taper Tom with the goose.
On went the farmer and the baker.

The baker tugged and tugged.
The farmer tugged and tugged.
They could not get away.

A shoemaker came down the road.
He saw Taper Tom and the goose.
He saw the farmer and the baker.
He laughed and laughed at them.

"Help!" called the baker.

The shoemaker ran to help the baker.

He tugged and tugged.

Taper Tom called, "Come with me."

The shoemaker could not get away.

On went Taper Tom and the goose.

On went the farmer and the baker.

On went the shoemaker.

The shoemaker tugged at the baker.
The baker tugged at the farmer.
The farmer tugged at the goose.
They could not get away.

A butcher came down the road.
He looked at Taper Tom and the goose.
He looked at the farmer and the baker.
He looked at the shoemaker.
He laughed and laughed.

"Where are you all going?"
said the butcher.

"We cannot get away from this goose,"
said the farmer.

"Help!" called the shoemaker.

The butcher ran to help them.

He tugged and tugged and tugged.

Taper Tom called, "Come with me."

The butcher could not get away.

On they all went to the castle.

The king's soldiers looked
at Taper Tom and the goose.
They looked at the farmer and the
baker. They looked at the shoemaker
and the butcher.

The soldiers laughed and laughed.

The king's cook looked out of a window
in the castle. She laughed and laughed.

"Help! Help!" called the butcher.

The cook ran out of the castle.

"I will help you," she called.

She tugged and tugged at the butcher.

Taper Tom called, "Come with me."

The cook could not get away.

She tugged at the butcher.

She could not get away.

"Help! Help!" called the cook.

The king looked out of his window.

The princess looked out of her window.

They saw Taper Tom and his goose.

They saw the baker with his cap.

They saw the farmer and the butcher.

They saw the shoemaker and the cook.

The king laughed and laughed.

Then he heard something. He heard
the princess. She was laughing, too.

The king called to Taper Tom.

He said, "You made the princess
laugh. You may have the princess
for your wife."

The princess went home
with Taper Tom.

Where the goose went, nobody knows.

Telling a Story

Tell the story of Taper Tom. Use the pictures on this page to help you.

The Pine Tree's Wishes

A little pine tree grew in the woods.
Big trees grew all around it.
The big trees had beautiful leaves.
The little pine tree had needles.

The little pine tree was not happy.
It did not want long needles.
It wanted beautiful leaves.

 "The Pine Tree's Wishes" adapted from "The Pine Tree" by Rose Dobbs from *Once Upon a Time* edited by Rose Dobbs. Copyright, 1950, by Random House, Inc.

One day the little pine tree
looked down. It said, "Something
has happened to me. I do not have
needles. I have leaves of gold.
I am beautiful now. No other tree
in the woods has leaves of gold.
Everyone who comes into the woods
will look at me."

The next day a man was walking
in the woods. He saw the little tree
with leaves of gold.

"What a beautiful tree," he said.
"It has leaves of gold. I will take
the gold leaves home with me."

The man walked over to the tree.
He took all the leaves off the tree.
He put them into his bag. Away he
went with his bag of gold leaves.

The little pine tree said,
"Why did I wish for leaves of gold?
I will not wish for leaves of gold
again. I wish I had leaves of glass."

The next day the little pine tree
looked down.

"Oh," said the little pine tree.
"How beautiful I am. I have glass
leaves. No other tree in the woods
has leaves of glass. Everyone who
comes into the woods will stop
to look at me."

That night the wind blew and blew.
It blew all around the little tree.

The glass leaves broke. They fell
all over the grass.

The next day the little pine tree
looked down.

"Oh," said the little tree.
"Look at my beautiful glass leaves.
Now I have no leaves. Why did I wish
for gold leaves? Why did I wish
for glass leaves? I wish I had
my long needles."

The next day the little pine tree
looked at its needles.

"Oh," said the little pine tree.
"I am happy. I have my needles again."

Do You Know?

1. A little pine tree lived in the woods.
It was not happy.

Why was the little pine tree not happy?

2. The little pine tree wished for leaves
of gold. A man saw the tree.

What did the man do?

3. The little pine tree wished for leaves
of glass. At night the wind blew.

What happened to the glass leaves?

4. At last the little pine tree
was happy.

Do you know why?

Words from the Story

leaves   pine tree   needles

Strange Footprints

It seemed that a giant
Tramped through the snow,
Or maybe an elephant—
No one would know.
Everyone guessed
Whose footprints could be,
But no one imagined
Galoshes and me!

Vivian Gouled

"Strange Footprints" by Vivian Gouled. Reprinted from
Humpty Dumpty's Magazine and used by permission of the author.

Mouths

I wish I had two little mouths
Like my two hands and feet—
A little mouth to talk with
And one that just could eat.

Because it seems to me mouths have
So many things to do—
All the time they want to talk
They are supposed to chew!

Dorothy Aldis

Playmaking Is Fun

Making Believe

Let's tell a story. This story
will not have words. You must tell
the story by using your arms
and legs and face.

First, look at the pictures of Tom
and Jane. These pictures show
what Tom and Jane like to do.

Now let the class know what *you* like
to do. How would you act it out?
Make your arms and legs and face
talk for you.

Here are pictures from some stories
you have read in this book.

Can you tell the name of each story?

Everyone likes to make believe.

Look at the pictures on this page.

Choose one of the stories to act.

Choose some part of the story that you
can act. You may want to ask a friend
to act in the story with you.

What will your hands show?

What will your feet do?

How will your face look?

More Playmaking

There are so many things for you
to play.

You can be a big bear or a little mouse.
You can be the strong wind or the tree
that moves in the wind.
You can be Taper Tom or a soldier.
You can be a boy who lives
at the North Pole.

Think about what you would like to be
and act it out for the class.

Poems to Play

Listen while your teacher reads
this poem to you.

The Ducks

When our ducks waddle to the pond,
They're awkward as awkward can be,
But when they get in the water and swim,
They glide most gracefully.

Alice Wilkins

"The Ducks" by Alice Wilkins, reprinted from *The Golden Flute*
by Hubbard and Babbitt, published by The John Day Company.

Two people may be the ducks. How do
the ducks walk? How do ducks swim?
Can you talk like a duck?

Here is a little poem for you to play.
Listen while your teacher reads
the poem to you.

The Three Little Kittens

Three little kittens lost their mittens;
  And they began to cry,
    "Oh, mother dear,
    We very much fear
  That we have lost our mittens."
    "Lost your mittens!
    You naughty kittens!
  Then you shall have no pie."

The three little kittens found their mittens;
And they began to cry,
"Oh, mother dear,
See here, see here!
See, we have found our mittens!"
"Put on your mittens,
You silly kittens,
And you may have some pie."
"Purr-r, purr-r, purr-r,
Oh, let us have some pie!
Purr-r, purr-r, purr-r."

The three little kittens put on
   their mittens;
      And soon ate up the pie.
         "Oh, mother dear,
         We greatly fear,
      That we have soiled our mittens!"
         "Soiled your mittens!
         You naughty kittens!"
      Then they began to sigh,
         "Mee-ow, mee-ow, mee-ow."

The three little kittens washed
    their mittens;
      And hung them out to dry;
        "Oh, mother dear,
        Do you not hear
    That we have washed our mittens?"
      "Washed your mittens!
      Oh, you're good kittens!
    But I smell a rat close by;
      Hush, hush! mee-ow, mee-ow."
    "We smell a rat close by,
      Mee-ow, mee-ow, mee-ow."

First, you will want to talk
about each part of the poem and
what it makes you see.

Then choose three boys and girls to be
the kittens. You will need someone
to be the mother cat. Who will be
the rat in the last part of the poem?

You may want to think about these
things before you begin to act:

1. What will I say?
2. What will I do?

Acting a Story

There are two parts to the story
on pages 100 and 101.
In Part 1 you are in the country.
In Part 2 you are in the town.

After you read the story you
may act it out. Talk about what the
Town Mouse might say. Talk about
what the Country Mouse might say.
How do you think they would act?

The Town Mouse and the Country Mouse

Part 1

A Town Mouse went to visit a
Country Mouse, who lived in a hole
in the barn.

As they were eating their dinner,
the Town Mouse said, "I do not like
your house. I would not like to live
in the country."

The Country Mouse said, "I like
to live in the country. I can hide
in the hay and no one can find me."

"Come home with me," said
the Town Mouse. "We will have cake
for our dinner. You will see
what a fine house I have."

Part 2

The next day the Country Mouse and
the Town Mouse went to a fine house,
where the Town Mouse lived.

The Country Mouse looked around
the beautiful house. He went
into the kitchen with the Town Mouse.

They found some bread and cake
to eat. The Country Mouse ate and ate.
Just then he heard the Town Mouse call,
"Run! Run! The cat is coming.
He will eat you."

The Town Mouse ran into his hole
in the wall. The Country Mouse
did not know what to do. He ran out
of the house and back to his home
as fast as he could go.

He knew he would be happy
in his little nest in the hay.

Making a Story into a Play

This is a story about Andrew and the red cap that his mother made for him. After you read about Andrew you will have fun making the story into a play.

Andrew's Red Cap

One day little Andrew said, "Mother, I wish I had a red cap."

"A red cap!" said his mother. "I will make a cap for you."

So she made a cap for Andrew.

Andrew put on his red cap.

"What a pretty cap!" he said. "How fine I look! Mother, I am going down the road. I want everyone to see my pretty red cap."

Away went Andrew down the road.

Andrew met Farmer Brown.

Farmer Brown looked at Andrew.

"Andrew, Andrew," he said. "I did not know you. How fine you look in your pretty red cap. Do you want to ride with me?"

"No, thank you," said Andrew. "I do not want to ride. I am going down the road. I want everyone to see my cap."

Andrew met a little girl.

"What a pretty cap!" she said.
"I wish I had a red cap. I will give you my bag for your pretty red cap."

"Oh, no!" said Andrew. "I want my red cap."

"I will give you my coat for your red cap," said the little girl.

"No, thank you," said Andrew.
"I want to show everyone my cap."

Away he ran on down the road.

Andrew met a little old woman.
She looked at Andrew's red cap.

"How fine you look!" she said.
"Are you going to see the king?"

"To see the king?" said Andrew.
"I will go to see the king. I want
him to see my red cap."

Andrew saw the king's castle.
He saw the princess in the garden.

"Oh, princess!" said Andrew.
"I am Andrew. I want to see the king.
I want to show him my red cap."

The princess looked at Andrew.
"What a pretty cap!" she said.
"Come with me. The king shall see
your cap."

The princess went into the castle.
Andrew went with her. His little
red cap was on his head.

"What a big, big castle," said
Andrew. "Where is the king?
Will I see him?"

"Yes, yes," said the princess.
Then she opened a big door. Andrew
and the princess went into a beautiful
big room.

"Sit down," said the princess.
"The king will soon be here. Then he
will look at your cap."

Andrew sat down with his cap
on his head.

"May I put your cap away?"
said the princess.

"Oh, no!" said Andrew. "The king
must see my cap. Everyone must see
my cap."

Andrew heard the door open.
He looked up. There was the king.

"Andrew came to see you," said
the princess. "He wants you to see
his red cap."

"What a fine cap!" said the king.
"I must have that cap. I will give you
my crown for your cap."

"No, thank you," said Andrew.
"I want my red cap. My mother
made it for me. Oh, I want my mother."

Away went Andrew out of the castle.

Andrew ran down the road.

On and on he ran. At last he came
to his mother's house.

Andrew was so happy to see his mother.

"Oh, Mother, the king wanted
my red cap. He wanted to give me
his crown for it. I did not give my cap
to the king. Was I foolish, Mother?"

"No, Andrew," said his mother.
"The king looks fine in his crown.
You look fine in your little red cap."

Making a Play

Let's make a play using the story
about Andrew. First, we will look
at the parts of the story.

▶ Read the first page of this story.
This page will tell what will happen
in the first part of the play.
Who is in this first part?
What happens in this part?

▶ Read page 103. This page will tell
what will happen in the second part
of your play.
Andrew meets Farmer Brown.
What does the old man say to Andrew?
What does Andrew do?

▶ Read page 104. This page tells
what will happen in the third part
of the play.
Who talks first in this part?
What does Andrew say to the little girl?

▶ Read page 105. Something happens
in this part that makes Andrew want
to go to the king's castle.

Who talks first in this part?

What does Andrew do?

▶ Read pages 106 and 107. This is a
long part. You will need three people
to act in this part.

Andrew talks to the princess
as they go into the castle.

The princess talks to the king
when he comes into the big room.

Then Andrew and the king talk.

What happens to Andrew at the end
of this part?

▶ Read the last page of the story.
In this part Andrew is at home.

He talks to his mother.

What will Andrew's mother say to him?

What do you think Andrew's mother
does as the play ends?

More Stories for Playmaking

Chippy Chipmunk Finds a Home

How do you think Chippy would look with nuts in his cheek?

The Run-Away Cows

Show what happened when the two cows jumped over the fence into the field.

900 Buckets of Paint

How did the little old woman and her animals look when they were unhappy? How did they look when they were happy?

Silly Matt

Show what happened when the milkman or the man with the goats met Matt.

The Friendly Tiger

Homer was a big, friendly tiger.
He lived in a pit in the zoo. Every day
the children came to see him. They
liked to look at him as he ran around
in the pit. The children talked to him.
They were not afraid of him.

"The Friendly Tiger" adapted by permission of David McKay Co., Inc. Copyright, 1952, by Katharine Wood.

One day Homer said, "I am going
to jump out of this pit. The children
come to see me. Now I will go
to see them."

Every day Homer tried to jump
out of the pit. One day he jumped,
and out of the pit he went.

Homer went down the street. He saw
a dog. He said, "The dogs that come
to the zoo are my friends. I have seen
that dog at the zoo."

Homer walked over to the dog.

"Grrr!" said the dog, and away he ran
as fast as he could go.

"That dog should know me,"
said Homer. "I have seen him
at the zoo."

Homer went on down the street.
He saw a cat.

"Oh, see that little tiger," said Homer.
"He will know me."

The cat saw Homer coming
down the street and away he went
up a tree.

"Why did he run away?" said Homer.
"Is he afraid of me? Where are
my friends who came to see me
at the zoo?"

Homer looked around. He said
to himself, "Where are the children
who live in this town? Many of them
come to see me at the zoo. They all
know me. They are all my friends."

Homer looked at the houses as he went
down the street. He said, "My friends
live in these houses. They will be
so happy to see me."

He stopped in front of one house.
He saw someone looking out
of the window.

"Some of my good friends may live
in this house," he said. "I will go
to see them."

As Homer went up to the house
he heard someone call, "Oh! Oh!
A tiger! A tiger! Do not go
near the window!"

Homer said, "The people in this house
do not know me. I will go to some
other house."

Homer went on down the street. He saw
a little boy near a house.

Homer said, "There is my friend
who comes to the zoo every day."

Homer walked over to the boy.

The little boy took one look at Homer
and away he ran into the house.

"Mother! Mother!" he called.
"A tiger! A tiger!"

"Christopher, why are you afraid?"
said his mother. "You know there are
no tigers around here. All the tigers
live in the zoo."

Christopher said, "Mother, look out
of the window! You will see a tiger!"

Christopher's mother looked out
of the window.

"Oh! Oh! There is a tiger
out there!" she said.

Christopher's mother called the police.
She said, "There is a tiger
on our street. Will you please
catch him?"

Homer walked on down the street.
Everyone who saw him ran away
calling, "A tiger! A tiger!"

Homer said, "Boys and girls come
to the zoo to see me. Why do they
run away now, when I come
to see them?"

"I wish I were back in my pit in the zoo," said Homer. "I cannot find my friends here."

Homer saw some men coming up the street.

He heard them say, "We will catch that tiger. We will take him back to the zoo."

Homer took one look at the men. Away he ran back to the zoo.

As he walked into the zoo, he could see his pit. He said, "I will not go away from the zoo again."

Homer jumped into his pit. He ate his dinner. Soon he was fast asleep.

Homer heard some men talking.
He jumped up. He wanted to see
what they were doing.

The men were putting a fence
around his pit.

One man said, "Homer will not jump
out of this pit again."

"I do not want a fence around my pit,"
said Homer to himself. "I will not go
to see my friends again. They can come
to see me."

Tell the Story

Look at the pictures and
tell the story of Homer.

The Monkey and the Turtle

One day a turtle was walking
down the road. He had some bananas.
A monkey up in a tree saw the turtle.

The monkey called, "Where did you get
the bananas? Please give me some."

"No," said the turtle. "I want
all the bananas for myself."

"The Monkey and the Turtle" by Charles H. Meeker, adapted from "Mr. Monk and Mr. Terra-
pin" from *Folk Tales of the Far East.*

"May I have one banana?" said the
monkey. "Please give me one banana."

"I will not give my bananas away,"
said the turtle. "You cannot have one
of them."

The monkey said to himself, "I will get
some of the bananas. I will play a trick
on that turtle."

The monkey ran up to the top of a tree.
He called down to the turtle, "I wish
you could climb to the top of this tree.
You could look all over the woods.
The world looks beautiful from the top
of a tree."

The turtle looked up at the monkey.

"What can you see from the top
of that tree?" he said.

"I see bees and birds," said
the monkey. "I see a big river.
I see some turtles near the river.
I see a town not far away. I see
all the animals in the woods."

The turtle said, "I wish that I could climb to the top of a tree. I wish that I could look around the woods."

The turtle put the bananas on the grass. He called to the monkey, "Can you help me climb up a tree?"

"Yes, I can help you climb a tree," said the monkey. He ran down the tree. "If I help you climb," he said, "you must give me four bananas."

"Oh, no," said the turtle. "I will not give you four bananas."

"Then give me three bananas," said the monkey.

"Oh, no," said the turtle. "I will not give you three bananas."

"Give me two bananas," said the monkey.

"No! No!" said the turtle. "I will not give you two bananas. I will give you one banana."

The monkey said, "Then give me one banana, and I will help you climb."

The turtle looked at his bananas.
He wanted to find a little one.
He gave a little banana to the monkey.
The monkey ate the banana.
"Now I will help you climb," he said.
"Take the end of my tail in your mouth.
Then walk up the tree with your claws."

The turtle caught the end
of the monkey's tail in his mouth.
The monkey began to climb the tree.

Up, up they went.

The turtle did not try to climb
the tree. He let the monkey pull him.

"We will never get to the top
of this tree," said the monkey
to himself. "Why did I tell
this silly turtle that I would help
him climb?"

The monkey looked down at the turtle.

"I said I would help you climb,"
he said. "I did not say that I would
pull you to the top of the tree.
Stick your claws into the tree
and climb."

"I gave you a banana to help me climb,"
said the turtle. "I do not want to climb.
I want you to pull me to the top
of the tree."

The monkey pulled and pulled to get
the turtle to the top of the tree.

At last the monkey said,
"Here we are at the top of the tree.
Now look around and see the world."

The turtle began to look around.

The monkey ran down the tree as fast
as he could go. The turtle was looking
around. He did not see the monkey
run away.

"I would like to live in a tree,"
said the turtle as he looked around.
"I could see what everyone is doing.
I like to be up where I can see
all over the woods."

The turtle talked and talked
to himself about what he could do
if he had a home in a tree.

After the turtle had looked around
for a long time he wanted to climb
down the tree. He wanted to get back
to the road again.

He said, "I want to climb down."
He looked around to find the monkey.
The monkey was not in the tree.

"Where are you, Mr. Monkey?"
called the turtle.

"Here I am," called the monkey
from under the tree.

"Come up here. I want to climb
down," called the turtle.

The monkey said, "I helped you climb up the tree. I did not say that I would help you climb down. You will have to get down by yourself."

The turtle called and called, but the monkey would not help him climb down.

At last the turtle called, "I will give you a banana if you will help me climb down."

"Will you give me two bananas?" asked the monkey.

"No, I will not give you two bananas," said the turtle. "I will give you one banana."

"Then jump down," called the monkey.

Can You Tell?

1. A turtle had some bananas.
A monkey wanted some of them.
What did the turtle say?

2. The monkey said, "I will play a trick
on that turtle."
What did the monkey do?

3. The turtle wished that he
could climb a tree, too.
How did the monkey help the turtle?

4. They began to climb the tree.
The monkey could not climb very fast.
Why couldn't he climb fast?

5. The turtle looked all around.
Then he wanted to climb down the tree.
Why didn't the monkey help him?

Words from the Story

banana

claws

Holding Hands

Elephants walking
Along the trails

Are holding hands
By holding tails.

Trunks and tails
Are handy things

When elephants walk
In circus rings.

Elephants work
And elephants play

And elephants walk
And feel so gay.

And when they walk—
It never fails

They're holding hands
By holding tails.

Lenore M. Link

"Holding Hands" by Lenore M. Link from the June, 1936
St. Nicholas Magazine.

134

Song for a Child

My kitty has a little song
She hums inside of her;
She curls up by the kitchen fire
And then begins to purr.

It sounds just like she's winding up
A tiny clock she keeps
Inside her beautiful fur coat
To wake her, when she sleeps.

Helen Bayley Davis

135

Mr. Bear's Tricks

Mr. Bear lived in the woods.
There was a big field near the woods.

Every morning Mr. Bear went
to the river to get a drink.
He always looked around the field
when he went to the river.

One morning Mr. Bear saw Mr. Coyote
in the field. Mr. Coyote was under a tree.

Mr. Bear called, "Hello, Mr. Coyote!
Are you asleep?"

"No, I am not asleep," said Mr. Coyote.
"I am thinking about what I will plant
in my garden."

"I am thinking about planting a garden,
too," said Mr. Bear.

"I will plant a garden with you,"
said Mr. Coyote.

Mr. Bear said, "Let us plant potatoes."

"I would like to plant potatoes,"
said Mr. Coyote.

The next morning Mr. Coyote and
Mr. Bear went into the field to plant
their garden.

Mr. Coyote said, "I will dig up
the ground with this stick."

Mr. Bear said, "I will plant
the potatoes."

Soon Mr. Coyote and Mr. Bear
had the potatoes planted.

Every day Mr. Coyote went to the garden
to see how the potatoes were growing.

Every day Mr. Bear went to the garden
to see how the potatoes were growing.

One day Mr. Coyote and Mr. Bear met
in the garden.

"The potatoes are growing,"
said Mr. Coyote. "I see some
little green stems."

One day when the potato plants
were big, Mr. Coyote saw Mr. Bear
in the garden.

Mr. Bear said, "Which part
of the potato plant do you want?
Do you want the part that grows
under the ground? Do you want
the part that grows above the ground?"

Mr. Coyote looked at the big green
stems above the ground. He said,
"I will take the part of the plant
that grows above the ground."

Mr. Bear laughed to himself.
He said, "I will take the part
that grows under the ground."

Days and days went by.

One morning Mr. Bear went
to the garden.

He said, "I think the potatoes are
big enough to eat. I will dig them up
and take them home with me."

Mr. Bear was in the garden
for a long time. He put all
of the potatoes into big bags. He took
each bag of potatoes to his home.

Mr. Coyote came to the garden.

He saw Mr. Bear walking away
with the last bag of potatoes.
He saw the tops of the potato plants
on the ground. He knew that Mr. Bear
had taken all of the potatoes.

Mr. Coyote called, "You have taken
all of the potatoes. There is nothing
in the garden for me to eat now."

Mr. Bear put his bag of potatoes
down. He said, "You wanted the part
of the potato plant that grows
above the ground. That is the part
of the potatoes that you see
in the garden now."

Mr. Bear walked away.

Mr. Coyote called, "You will not play
this trick on me again."

The next spring Mr. Coyote walked
into the woods to find Mr. Bear.
He met Mr. Bear by the river.

"Hello, Mr. Bear," called Mr. Coyote.
"It is time for us to plant another
garden. I am going to take
the part of the plant that grows
under the ground. You may take the
part that grows above the ground."

Mr. Bear said, "What shall we plant
this time? Shall we plant corn?"

Mr. Coyote looked at Mr. Bear.
"I like corn," he said. "Let us plant
some corn. Let us go to the garden
in the morning."

The next morning Mr. Bear and
Mr. Coyote met in the garden.
All day long they planted corn.

Day after day Mr. Bear went
to the garden. He wanted to see
how the corn was growing.

Day after day Mr. Coyote went
to the garden. He wanted to see
how the corn was growing.

One day Mr. Bear was in the garden.
He said, "This corn must be picked.
I will pick the ears of corn and take
them home."

Mr. Bear went from corn stalk
to corn stalk. He picked all the ears
of corn. He put the corn into bags.
He took the bags of corn to his home.

The next day Mr. Coyote went
to the garden. He looked around to find
the corn. There was no corn on the stalks.

Mr. Coyote said, "Mr. Bear has taken
all the ears of corn. I will eat
my part of the corn now. I will eat
the part that grows under the ground."

Mr. Coyote began to dig. He took
the part of the corn stalk that grows
under the ground. Then he sat down
to eat it.

"Oh!" he said. "This part of the corn
is not good to eat. Mr. Bear played
another trick on me."

Mr. Coyote ran into the woods to find Mr. Bear. He saw him under a tree.

Mr. Coyote called, "You have played another trick on me."

Mr. Bear looked up. "You asked for the part of the corn that grows under the ground," he said.
"Now go home and eat it."

Telling a Story

Find the sentence that tells what happened first in the story. Which sentence tells what happened next? Put each sentence in the right place.

1. Mr. Bear said, "Let us plant potatoes."

2. Mr. Bear picked all of the ears of corn and took them home.

3. Mr. Bear put all of the potatoes into big bags.

4. Mr. Coyote could not eat the part of the corn stalk that grows under the ground.

5. Mr. Coyote said, "I will take the part of the plant that grows above the ground."

Lucky Hans

Hans worked for a shoemaker.
His mother lived in a little town
far down the road. He had not seen her
for a long time.

One day Hans said to the shoemaker,
"I have worked for you for a long time.
I want to go home to see my mother.
Please, may I go?"

"Yes, you may go," said the shoemaker.
"I will give you your money.
I will put the money in a bag, and
you may take it home with you."

The shoemaker put the money in a bag
and gave it to Hans. Then Hans
started down the road for home.

As he walked down the road he met
a man with a horse. Hans stopped
to look at the horse.

"What a fine horse," he said
to himself. "I wish I had a horse
that I could ride. I would soon be
home."

The man on the horse looked at Hans.
"What is in your bag?" he asked.

Hans said, "I have all the money
that the shoemaker gave to me.
I would give all the money in this bag
for your horse."

"Let me see your money," said the man.

Hans gave the bag to the man.
He said, "You may have the money
if you will give me your horse."

The man looked at the money and
he said, "You may have the horse."

The man got off the horse and helped
Hans get on the horse's back.

"If you want the horse to go fast,
you say 'Gee-up'," said the man.

"Thank you," said Hans. "I will say
'Gee-up' when I want the horse
to go fast."

Hans started down the road
on the horse.

"How lucky I am," he said.
"Now it will not take me very long
to get home."

The horse did not go very fast.

Hans called, "Gee-up! Gee-up!"

When Hans said "Gee-up," the horse
ran as fast as he could go.

The horse ran so fast that Hans
went up and down on the horse's back.

"Stop!" called Hans, but the horse
would not stop. He ran faster and
faster.

Hans called again, "Stop! Stop!"
but the horse would not stop.

"Oh!" said Hans, "I cannot ride
on this horse. How can I stop him?"

Hans fell off the horse's back.

The horse ran on as fast as
he could go.

A farmer was coming down the road
with a cow. He saw the horse running
away.

"Whoa! Whoa!" called the farmer.

The horse stopped.

The farmer took the horse back
to Hans.

"Here is your horse," he said.

"I will never ride that horse again,"
said Hans. "I wanted to ride fast
so I said 'Gee-up!' He ran so fast
that I could not sit on his back.
I called 'Stop!' He would not stop."

"He is a fine horse," said the farmer.
"You do not know how to ride him.
When you want a horse to stop
you say 'Whoa.' You do not say 'Stop.'
I want a horse. I will give you my cow
for your horse."

"You may have the horse," said Hans.
"I will take your cow."

Hans gave the horse to the man.
The man gave the cow to Hans.

155

"How lucky I am to have a cow,"
said Hans as he went on down the road.
"Now Mother and I will have
all the milk that we can drink."

Hans walked on with his cow.

After a long time he said, "I want
a drink. I know what I will do.
I will milk my cow."

Hans stopped and tied the cow
to a tree. He walked around and
around the cow. He had never milked
a cow. He did not know where to sit.

At last Hans got down on one knee.
He started to milk the cow.

The cow did not want Hans
to milk her. She looked around at him.
She kicked him and over he went
into the road.

Hans sat in the road and looked
at the cow.

A man came down the road with a pig.
He saw Hans in the road. He said,
"Why do you sit in the road?"

"I started to milk my cow," said Hans.
"She kicked me into the road."

"You do not know how to milk a cow,"
said the man. "I know how to milk
a cow. Give me your cow, and you
may have my pig."

"Take the cow," said Hans, "and give me
your pig. I am happy to give away
that cow."

Hans gave the cow to the man.
The man gave the pig to Hans.

Hans went on down the road
with his pig. The pig could not walk
fast.

Hans said, "I wish that I could give
this pig away."

Hans met an old man with a goose
under his arm.

"How would you like to give me
your goose for my pig?" said Hans.

"I would like to have a pig,"
said the old man.

Hans gave the pig to the old man.
The old man gave the goose to Hans.

"How lucky I am to have this goose,"
said Hans.

Hans put the goose under his arm and on he went.

At last he came to a town.

As he walked into the town, he saw a man near a house. A big stone was in front of the man.

"What do you do with that big stone?" said Hans.

"I sharpen scissors on this stone," said the man. "That is how I make my money."

"I wish I had your stone,"
said Hans. "I could sharpen scissors.
Then I would make some money."

The man said, "Give me your goose.
You may have the stone."

Hans gave the man the goose and
the man gave him the stone. Hans put
the stone on his back and away he went.

"How lucky I am," said Hans. "Now I
will sharpen scissors. I will make
some money."

Hans walked on with the big stone
on his back.

He said, "I will soon come to the river.
Then I will have a drink of water."

When Hans got to the river, he put
his hands into the water to get
a drink. The stone fell off his back.
It fell into the water.

Hans looked at the big stone
in the water. "How lucky I am!"
he said. "I do not have to carry
that big stone. I can walk fast
and I will soon be home."

Telling a Story

Hans started down the road
with a bag of money. When Hans
got home, he had no money.

The pictures on this page show parts
of the story. Each picture shows
something that happened to Hans
on his way home.

Look at the pictures and tell the story
of Lucky Hans.

900 Buckets of Paint

There was an old woman who lived
in a little red house. The rain
had taken the paint off the house
so that it looked very old.

One day the little old woman said,
"I am going to move out of this old
house. I want to live in a new house."

The next morning the old woman called
her two cats that were in the attic
of the house. She put the cats
into a cart. She put all of her things
into the cart. Then she looked
around the house.

She said, "I have all of my things
in the cart now."

She did not know that she forgot
to take her clock that was
in the cupboard.

She tied her cow to the back
of the cart. Then she called
her donkey.

"Come, Arthur," she said.
"We are going to move. We are going
to look for another house. I want you
to pull the cart."

Away they went down the road.

After they had gone a long way,
the old woman saw a little brown house.

She stopped the donkey so that she
could look at the little brown house.

The little old woman said, "I like
this house. I like the garden."

Then she looked into the house.
She said, "No one lives here.
We will live in this house."

The old woman took all of her things
out of the cart. She put them
in the brown house.

The next morning the little old woman looked all around the house. She said, "I like this house. We will be happy here."

She called her cats that were up in the attic. She said, "Do you like this house?"

The cats said, "We like to live here. We caught so many mice last night."

The next morning the old woman took
a bucket of water out to the donkey.

She said, "Arthur, do you like to live
here?"

The donkey said, "I do not like
to live here. There is no pond.
I will not drink out of a bucket.
I want to drink out of a pond."

The old woman said to herself,
"Arthur is not happy. We must find
a house where there is a pond."

The little old woman put all
of her things in the cart. She put
the two cats in the cart. She tied
the cow to the back of the cart.
She called the donkey.

"Come, Arthur," she said. "Come
and pull the cart. We are going
to look for a house where there is
a pond."

Away went the little old woman
down the road with all of her animals.

On and on they went.

At last, far down the road,
the old woman saw a green house.
There was a big pond near the house.

The old woman stopped at this house
and looked in one of the windows.
She said, "No one lives here.
We may like this house."

She took all of her things out
of the cart and put them in the green
house.

The next morning the little old woman
went out to milk the cow. The cow
would not give any milk.

The woman looked at the cow and said,
"Why don't you give me some milk?"

The cow said, "I do not like to live
here. I like to eat clover."

The little old woman said, "There is
green grass near the pond."

"I know there is green grass
near the pond," said the cow.
"I do not want to eat grass. I want
to eat clover."

The next morning the little old woman
put all of her things into the cart again.

She called the two cats, the donkey,
and the cow.

She said, "Bossy does not like it here.
We are going to look for another house.
It must have a field of clover and
a pond near it."

Off they went to find another house.
Arthur pulled the cart down the road.
On and on they went.

At last the little old woman saw
a little house. She did not like
the house, but there was a big field
of clover and a pond near it.

"We will stop here," said the old woman.

She looked all around the house.
She looked in a window.

"No one lives in this house," she said.
"We will move into this house. We will
all be happy here."

The little old woman took all of her
things out of the cart. She moved them
into the house.

The next morning the little old woman
went out to milk the cow. Bossy was
eating clover and she was very happy.

The old woman took the bucket of milk
to the house. She called the two cats
and said, "I have some good milk
for you."

The cats would not drink the milk.

The little old woman said, "Drink
your milk."

"We do not like this house,"
said the cats. "There is no attic here.
We cannot find any mice."

The little old woman said, "My cats
must be happy. They must have mice
to eat. We will move again."

The little old woman called the donkey
and all the animals to her. She said,
"We will have to move. My cats
are not happy here. We are going
to find a house where everyone
will be happy."

The very next morning the old woman
put the cats and all of her things
into the cart again.

Away they went down the road to find
another house.

The little old woman said,
"We must find a house where everyone
will be happy."

On and on down the road went
the little old woman and her animals.

At last the old woman saw a house
where nobody lived. It was
a white house. It had a big attic.
There was a field of clover and a pond
near the house.

The old woman called,
"Arthur, stop here." Then she said,
"We will look at this house. I think
we will all be happy in this house."

The little old woman saw a man
walking around the house. He had
a bucket of white paint.

"Good morning," said the old woman.
"Do you live here?"

"No, I do not live here," said the man.
"I have painted this house. A friend
gave me nine hundred buckets of paint.
Some of the houses around here looked
old, so I painted all of them."

The old woman looked at the house
again. She looked at the yard.

"May I move in here with my two cats,
my cow, and my donkey?" said the
old woman.

"Yes," said the man. "We will be
very happy to have you live here."

The little old woman went
into the house and looked around.
She looked in a cupboard. She saw
a clock.

"This looks like my old clock,"
she said. The little old woman
looked all around the house.

She said, "Why, this is my old
red house. The man painted it white.
He made it look like a new house."

The little old woman called
to her animals.

She said, "We are going to live here.
There is an attic for the cats.
There is a big field of clover
for Bossy. There is a pond nearby
for Arthur. I know we will all
be happy in our old home."

Can You Tell?

1. The little old woman and
her animals moved from house to house.
   Why was Arthur unhappy?
   Why was Bossy unhappy?
   Why were the cats unhappy?

2. At last they saw a white house.
A man said that they could live in it.
   What was the man doing?

3. Everyone liked the white house.
The little old woman looked
in a cupboard.
   What did she find?

Words from the Story

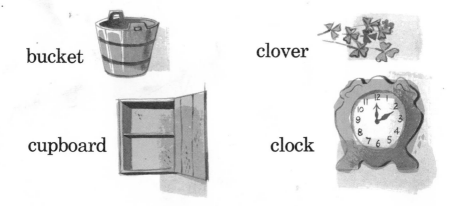

bucket

clover

cupboard

clock

Silly Matt

Matt and his mother lived
in a little house near a river.
Every day Matt went down
to the river. He liked to sit
under a tree to look at the people
as they went down the road
into the town.

One day Matt's mother said, "Matt, you sit around all day. Why don't you put a bridge over the river? Everyone who goes over the bridge will pay toll and you will make some money."

"I will put a bridge over the river," said Matt. "I will start to work today."

Matt worked for days and days.

At last he had a fine bridge over the river. He sat down to take toll from the people who went over the bridge.

The first man to go over the bridge
was a man with some hay.

"Good morning," said the man.
"What a fine bridge you have made.
We have wanted a bridge for a
long time."

"Everyone who goes over the bridge
must pay toll," said Matt.
"I will make some money now."

"I have no money for my toll,"
said the man with the hay.

Matt said, "Give me some of your hay."

"I will," said the man. "I will put
some hay on the grass near the bridge."

Soon an old man with a bag went
over the bridge.

"This is a very fine bridge," he said.

"Yes," said Matt. "You must pay toll."

"I have no money for my toll.
What can I give you?" said the old man.

"What do you have in your bag?"
asked Matt.

"I have some needles," said the man.
"I will give you two needles for my toll."

"I will take the needles to my mother,"
said Matt.

The man gave Matt two needles.

Matt did not know what to do
with the needles so he put them
in the hay.

When it was time to go home, Matt
looked at the hay.

He said, "How can I take this hay
home? I cannot carry it on my back.
I will throw the hay into the river.
Then I will go home."

As Matt walked up the road
to his home he met his mother.

"Oh, Matt!" she called.
"I have waited and waited for you.
What did you get for toll today?"

"One man gave me some hay,"
said Matt. "Another man gave me
two needles."

"What did you do with the hay and
the needles?" asked his mother.

"The man who gave me the hay put it
on the grass by the bridge," said Matt.
"I put the needles in the hay.
I did not know how to carry the hay,
so I threw it into the river."

"Oh, Matt! You silly boy," said
his mother. "Now you have no hay,
and you have no needles. Next time
put the hay on the bridge.
Put the needles in your cap."

"I will do as you say next time,"
said Matt.

The next day a baker went
over the bridge with some bags
of flour.

"Your toll, please," said Matt.

"I have no money," said the baker.
"I will give you some of my flour."

"Please put the flour on my bridge,"
said Matt.

The baker put some of the flour
on the bridge.

When Matt got home his mother was
at the door waiting for him.

"Matt, what did you get for toll?"
she said.

"I got some flour from a baker,"
said Matt.

"Where is the flour?" said his mother.

"The baker put the flour on the bridge,"
said Matt.

"Oh, Matt," said his mother,
"you silly boy. I told you to put the hay
on the bridge. When you get flour
for toll, carry it home in a bucket."

The next day a shoemaker went
over the bridge.

"May I have your toll?" said Matt.

"I have no money," said the shoemaker.
"I will give you my scissors."

"I would like your scissors," said Matt.
"I will put them in my cap."

Matt put the scissors in his cap and
started for home.

When Matt came into the house
his mother saw something in his cap.

"Matt, what is in your cap?" she said.

"Scissors," said Matt. "A shoemaker
gave me the scissors, and I put them
in my cap."

"Oh, Matt," said his mother, "I told you
to put the needles in your cap.
Always put scissors in your pocket."

"Mother, I will do as you say
next time," said Matt.

The next day a milkman walked
over the bridge. He had two buckets
of milk.

He put his two buckets of milk down
on the bridge. He looked at Matt.

"I have no toll," he said, "but I
will give you some of my milk."

"I would like some milk," said Matt.

"Where will I put it?" said the milkman.

"Put the milk in my pockets,"
said Matt.

"You are a silly boy to put milk
in your pockets," said the man.

When Matt got home, his mother
was waiting for him.

"Matt," said his mother, "why did you
put milk in your pockets? Matt, why
did you put milk in your shoes?"

"A milkman gave me some milk
for his toll," said Matt. "I told him
to put the milk in my pockets.
The milk ran into my shoes."

"Oh, Matt! I told you to put
the scissors in your pocket," said
his mother. "Put milk in a bucket."

The next day, a man came
over the bridge with two little goats.

"I have no money for my toll,"
said the man. "I will give you one
of my goats."

"I would like to have a little goat,"
said Matt.

The man tied one goat to a tree.
Then he went on down the road.

When it was time to go home,
Matt said to himself, "How will I take
this goat home?"

Matt looked around. He saw
an old bucket by the bridge.

"I know what I will do," he said.
"I will carry the goat home
in that bucket."

Matt put the goat in the bucket and
started for home.

Matt's mother met him as he came
up the road. She saw the goat
in the bucket.

"Oh, Matt," she said. "That is not
the way to bring a goat home.
When you want to make a goat
go home, take a branch from a tree.
Make the goat run in front of you."

The next morning, a farmer walked over the bridge. He had some butter that he was taking into town.

"Your toll, please," said Matt.

"I have no money," said the farmer. "I will give you some butter for my toll."

The farmer gave Matt some of the butter.

Matt ran to get a branch from a tree.
He put the butter on the branch.
He put the branch near the river.
Then he sat down on the bridge.

The butter was in the sun all day.
There was no butter on the branch
by the time Matt started for home.

Matt walked home pulling the branch behind him.

"Matt, what did you get for toll today?" asked his mother.

"I got some butter," said Matt.

"Where is the butter?" asked his mother.

Matt looked around at the branch. There was no butter on it.

"I did have some butter," said Matt. "Where is it?"

"Oh, Matt," said his mother. "After this I will go to the bridge to take the toll."

Match Them

Here are pictures of the tolls
that the people gave to Matt:

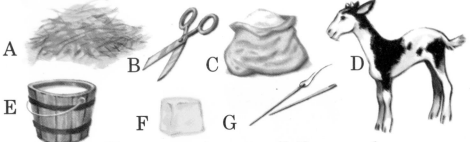

Here are pictures of the people
who gave Matt their tolls:

Match the letters and the numbers
to show who gave each of the tolls.
Tell what Matt did with each toll.

Some Things That Easter Brings

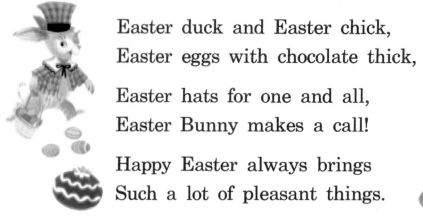

Easter duck and Easter chick,
Easter eggs with chocolate thick,

Easter hats for one and all,
Easter Bunny makes a call!

Happy Easter always brings
Such a lot of pleasant things.

Elsie Parrish

"Some Things That Easter Brings" by Elsie Parrish from *The Youth's Companion*.

Clouds

Two little clouds one April day
   Went sailing across the sky.
They went so fast they bumped their heads,
   And both began to cry,
The big round sun came out and said,
   "Oh, never mind, my dears,
I'll send all my sunbeams down
   To dry your fallen tears."

Stars

I'm glad the stars are over me
And not beneath my feet,
Where we should trample on them
Like cobbles on the street.
I think it is a happy thing
That they are set so far;
It's best to have to look up high
When you would see a star.

The Sleepy Tulips

Each evening tulips close their eyes
When the dew begins to fall;
I wonder if they really sleep,
They stand so straight and tall.
I couldn't sleep if I stood up—
A soft white bed holds me.
But all the day I run and play,
While tulips rest, you see!

Marion Mitchell Walker

"The Sleepy Tulips" by Marion Mitchell Walker from *Normal Instructor and Primary Plans*, published by *The Instructor*.

Paddy Bear's Christmas

Paddy Bear was a little brown bear. He lived in a cave in a hill far back in the woods.

Paddy lived with Mother Bear and Father Bear. He lived with Uncle Bear and Aunt Bear. They all lived in the cave in the hill far back in the woods.

All day long Paddy Bear played by himself around the cave. He climbed up the trees. He rolled down the hill.

One day Paddy Bear said to himself, "I am going to climb to the top of this hill. I want to see what is on the other side of the hill."

Paddy Bear did not tell Mother Bear where he was going.

204

Paddy started to climb the hill.
He looked up. He could see the top
of the hill. Paddy climbed and
climbed. Up, up he went.

At last he got to the top of the hill.
Paddy looked down the other side
of the hill. He started to run.
He ran so fast that he fell down.
Over and over he rolled.

Paddy Bear bumped into a big tree.
He got up and looked around. He saw
a little white house. He saw a window
in the house. He walked over
to the house and looked in the window.

"Oh!" said Paddy Bear. "I see
some people. Father Bear has always
told me to run away from people.
I will hide near this window. No one
will see me here."

Paddy heard the people saying,
"Merry Christmas! Merry Christmas!"
He looked in the window again.
A man and a boy were putting things
on a tree. They were saying,
"Merry Christmas! Merry Christmas!"
Paddy Bear walked away
from the house. He started back
to the cave.

Paddy Bear said, "What is
Merry Christmas? My father will know.
I will ask him."

When Paddy got back to the cave he ran
to Father Bear.

"I want to know what Merry Christmas is,"
Paddy said.

"I do not know what Merry Christmas is,"
said Father Bear. "Ask your mother.
She may know what Merry Christmas is."

Paddy Bear said, "Mother, I want
to know what Merry Christmas is."

"I do not know," said Mother Bear.

Paddy said, "How can I find out
what Merry Christmas is?"

Paddy began to cry.

"Why are you crying?" said Uncle Bear.

"I want to know what Christmas is,"
said Paddy Bear.

"Where did you hear about Christmas?"
asked Uncle Bear.

Paddy stopped crying.

Paddy said, "I went down the other side
of the hill. I saw a house. I looked
in a window in the house. I heard
people saying, 'Merry Christmas.'
I want to know what Merry Christmas is."

Paddy began to cry again.

"Stop crying," said Uncle Bear.
"I will go down to the house
on the other side of the hill.
I will find out what Christmas is."

Uncle Bear went down the hill.
He saw the little house. He looked
in a window. He saw people putting
things on a tree. The people were
putting green branches on the windows
and the doors of the house.

Uncle Bear heard the people saying,
"Merry Christmas, Merry Christmas!"

Uncle Bear climbed up the hill.
He went back to the cave and called,
"Paddy, Paddy. Come here! Come here!"
Paddy ran to Uncle Bear. "I know
what Christmas is now," said Uncle Bear.
"Christmas is putting green branches
on the doors and the windows
of a house."

Paddy Bear went into the woods.
He found some green branches.

Paddy Bear went back to the cave
with the green branches. He put them
all around the cave.

Mother Bear looked around the cave.
She said, "How pretty the cave is now."

Paddy Bear looked at the green
branches all around the cave. He said,
"Uncle Bear does not know what
Christmas is. Christmas is not putting
green branches around our homes.
Father does not know what Christmas is.
Mother does not know what Christmas is.
I want to know what Christmas is.
How can I find out what Christmas is?"

Paddy Bear began to cry again.

"Do not cry, Paddy," said Aunt Bear.
"I will go down the hill. I will go
to the little house. I will find out
what Christmas is."

Aunt Bear went down the other side
of the hill to the house. She looked
in the window. She saw a man and
a woman in the house. She saw children
looking at presents.

Aunt Bear said, "Now I know
what Christmas is. Christmas is getting
presents. I will find a present
for Paddy. I will take it to him."

Aunt Bear climbed the hill and
went back to the cave.

"Paddy, Paddy," she called. "Now
I know what Christmas is. Christmas
is getting presents. Here is a present
for you," she said.

Aunt Bear gave Paddy some honey.

"Oh, thank you," said Paddy Bear.
He ate the honey.

Paddy Bear looked around the cave.
He said, "Mother Bear did not get
a present. Father Bear did not get
a present. Christmas is not getting
presents. Can someone find out what
Merry Christmas is?" Paddy began
to cry.

Mother said, "Do not cry, Paddy.
I will go to the little house
on the other side of the hill. I will
find out what Christmas is."

Mother Bear went down the hill.
She looked in the window of the little
house.

Mother Bear saw the father and mother
who lived in the little house. She saw
the children. They were all very happy.
She heard the father say, "Christmas
is not getting presents. Christmas is
giving presents. Christmas is giving
something to others to make them happy."

Mother heard everyone say,
"Merry Christmas! Merry Christmas!"

Mother Bear climbed up the hill
as fast as she could go. She ran
into the cave.

"Paddy, Paddy!" she called. "I know
what Christmas is. I heard the people
in the house say, 'Christmas is giving
to others. Christmas is making people
happy.' "

Paddy ran out of the cave. He went
into the woods. He found a big stick
for Father Bear.

"This stick will help Father when he
climbs up the hill," said Paddy.

He found some nuts for Uncle Bear.
He found a pretty red feather
for Aunt Bear. He found some
long grass. He sat down and made
a broom for Mother Bear.

"Now I have something for everyone,"
he said.

Paddy ran into the cave. He said,
"I have Christmas for all of you."

Paddy gave Father Bear the big stick.

"Thank you," said Father Bear.
"This stick is what I wanted."

Paddy gave Aunt Bear the red feather.
He gave Uncle Bear the nuts.

"Oh! Thank you, Paddy," they said.
They were very happy with their
presents.

Paddy gave Mother Bear the broom
that he had made.

Mother Bear looked at him and said,
"How did you know that I wanted
a broom?" She gave Paddy a big
bear hug.

Paddy was so happy that he called,
"Merry Christmas! Merry Christmas!"

Can You Tell?

1. Paddy asked his Uncle Bear,
"What is Merry Christmas?"
What did Uncle Bear tell Paddy?

2. Then Paddy asked his Aunt Bear,
"What is Merry Christmas?"
What did Aunt Bear tell him?

3. Paddy Bear found presents
for everyone.
What were they?

4. At last Paddy Bear found out
what Merry Christmas is.
What is it?

5. Make believe that Paddy Bear asked
you to tell him about Christmas trees.
What would you say?

Words from the Story

present

broom

branches

feather

The Story Train

WORD LIST

STORY TRAIN uses a total of 548 words, 387 of which are common to most pre-primers, primers, and first-grade readers. 303 of these words have appeared in STORY WAGON and STORY TIME, the primer and first-grade reader in this series. The 161 words which may require some preparation are listed below in the order of their appearance. A star (°) indicates words introduced in this book which are typical second-grade words.

Poetry is excluded from the word list. Direction words used in the playmaking unit are also excluded but may be found in the teacher's manual for STORY TRAIN.

Page		Page		Page		Page	
6	Timothy	24	. . .	46	. . .		shall°
	river°	25	weasel	47	claws		people°
7	climb°	26	fence°	48	. . .	67	soldiers
	slide		front°	49	. . .		wife°
8	started°	27	outside°	50	. . .	68	magic
	muddy		through°	51	. . .		anyone°
	turn°	28	found°	52	. . .	69	. . .
	tried°		dinner°	53	. . .		
9	trying°	29	. . .			70	farmer°
10	. . .	30	. . .			71	baker°
11	. . .	31	. . .	54	rubbers	72	shoemaker°
12	woodchuck	32	. . .		Mrs. Goose°	73	. . .
13	. . .	33	. . .		closet	74	butcher
14	falls°	34	. . .	55	. . .	75	. . .
15	. . .	35	. . .	56	. . .	76	. . .
16	. . .			57	. . .	77	cook°
17	. . .	36	milk°	58	bed°	78	. . .
		37	say°		pillow	79	laughing°
18	Chippy		automobile	59	Mrs. Sheep°	80	. . .
	Chipmunk		or°	60	raining°	81	page
	move°	38	dry	61	behind°		pictures°
19	cheek	39	. . .	62	. . .	82	pine
	orchard	40	. . .	63	umbrella		grew°
20	skunk	41	. . .		hand°		leaves°
	grass°	42	. . .	64	plop		needles
	picked°	43	words°	65	. . .	83	gold
21	. . .					84	glass°
22	. . .	44	crab	66	Taper Tom	85	wind°
23	. . .	45	race°		princess		blew°
					castle		

223

224